get your bother on

A **Guided Journal** to Discover What's Next

Created for you by
Jennifer Louden

Table of Contents

First things first: reject perfectionism. Write something here in your most illegible handwriting. Or smear a little of your lunch on the page. Paste in fruit or veggie stickers. Or find a photograph of yourself that you love and doodle on it. Give yourself antennas, a halo, or...?

Thoughts on Using this Journal

This journal is not about finding THE answer. If you go in search of a specific *what's next*, you'll short-circuit the renewal you need to experience to get your bother on. *What's next* is not a destination; it's not about your career, a cause, a community, or creative work. It might involve those things, but *what's next* is far beyond any of those. *What's next* is whole-hearted contact and life immersion. *What's next* is to become more human, or as Stephen Colbert said in an interview with Anderson Cooper, "What's the point of being here and being human, if you can't be the most human you can be?" Let the idea of needing THE answer go.

Forget being neat and looking for the right answers. There are no answers! There are only musings, explorations, and experiments. Embrace this journal as a space to get curious and messy. Cross out sentences, use different ink colors, doodle, paste in bits and pieces of your life, insert scribbled notes to yourself, or even break the spine of the book (wild, I know). Getting your bother on is not neat or Instagram-pretty. It's about letting life in!

Order is not important. Yes, there are stages to bothering, but hey, is life ever linear? Skip what bores you, circle back to what scares you, revisit pages and add your thoughts.

If you like dates, use them. If not, don't.

Feel free to change, cross out, or rewrite prompts. Write your own. Everything is open to interpretation.

Why not consider all mediums? Keep a glue stick, tape, stapler, different colored pens and pencils, scraps of magazines, photos, and/or stickers nearby. *Or not.*

Perfectionism, rules, needing to know, trying to make the *right* plan, or being ruled by shoulds will not help you get your bother on. Listening, playing, daring, wondering, and desiring *will*.

In *Why Bother? Discover the Desire for What's Next*, I map out an approach to help you know where you are and where you can go. I've duplicated those stages in this journal, not because you have to get somewhere to start bothering (you are bothering now!), but to remind you that the natural creative process of life is always working on your behalf, and these are ways to collaborate with it.

The stages are:

1. Take stock
Where are you now? What's good, what's working, what's bugging you, what's wanting to fall away, what needs to stay the same? Get the lay of the land.

2. Leave behind
See with love and acceptance what needs to be jettisoned, forgiven, or let go, so you can free your energy to move forward.

3. Ease in
Generate wonder, awaken self-compassionate grit, investigate habits that deaden possibility, and celebrate your life force growing more vibrant.

4. Settle
What gets in the way of finding the stillness that makes everything else possible? What supports settling in and being?

5. Desire
The heart of the *get your bother on* approach. Make friends with the often misunderstood quality and energy of desire, replace substitute desires, soften fears of desire, and discern between grasping and growing.

6. Become by doing
Expand your emotional immune system, try out Conditions of Enoughness, and design ways to anchor your desire in the here and now. Get into action and let action change you.

7. Be seen
Celebrate your desires in the community of your choosing and take refuge in belonging.

take stock

The Take Stock stage of getting your bother on is all about seeing and feeling the good that is in your life now, touching the unchanging goodness and warmth at your core, recognizing the many ways you are already bothering, and celebrating the experience and talent you will be drawing on for what's next.

I'm not trying to jolly you into believing everything is fine, but rather helping you notice all that you have to build on and with, and to ignite faith in your own experiences and acquired wisdom.

This stage is also about naming what it might be time to let go of, whether that's a dream, a belief, or a habit of being cruel to yourself.

Taking stock helps you get curious about how and where you might be closing yourself off to life, while remembering that life never closes itself off from you. To feel life knocking at the door and begging you to open up.

Take a loving breath and know that bothering is in progress, and more life, more living, more creativity, more connection is already happening. You are already getting your bother on.

For inspiration and lists, check out jenniferlouden.com/whybother
and click on Settle for a list of movies and books.

GET YOUR BOTHER ON: TAKE STOCK **2**

GATHER STORIES

Gather stories about how making a life that feels good and
alive is always a process of reinvention. Collect titles of movies,
novels, friends' stories, or whatever reminds you here.

Collect more stories focused on the moment when someone woke up and faced the fact something had to change. Some of my favorites include *Fried Green Tomatoes, Enchanted April, Little Women, Frankie and Grace,* and *The Midnight Library.*

GATHER STORIES

What are my best memories of bothering?
*Make a timeline of key life moments. How did you
bother as a child? A teen? A young adult? In your first
job? When falling in love?*

What five words describe the story
I am living right now.

What five words describe the
story I want to live?

REASONS TO BOTHER

Keeping your promises to yourself

Smell of crayons and new books

Kind notes given for no reason

Mary Oliver poems read aloud by a blackwater pond

Thwack of a tennis ball

Pinion wood fire on a chilly morning

ABBA singalongs

Fears shared

Spring training

Fat Bear Week

Sweet peas grown from seed

Bach's "Violin Partita No. 2"

Castle ruins

Finishing something difficult and feeling pride

Ancient redwoods

Harriet the Spy and *The Phantom Tollbooth*

Baby panda videos sent to a friend in need

Warm water

Monty Python sketches

Libraries

Museé d'Orsay

Now name some of your own reasons.
Think small, sensual, shared with others. Come back
here often and add to this page.

UNMAKING & REMAKING

David Whyte writes in *Crossing the Unknown Sea*, "Often, in order to stay alive, we have to unmake a living in order to get back to living the life we wanted for ourselves. It is this cycle of making, disintegration, and remaking that is the hallmark of meaningful and creative work."

What unmaking might I be in the midst of? Can I see this as part of my life's cycle?

What aspects of my unmaking
am I excited about?

And that's because...

WHY BOTHER?

When I accept that feeling lost, adrift, stuck, bored, even despairing, is a normal, recurring, and vital part of a well-lived life, when I accept that asking "why bother?" is baked into being human, I find myself wondering what if... *What if being lost is showing you something important about what you're hungry to change? What if boredom needs to be investigated for its treasures? What if feeling happy all the time is a depressing, impossible standard and it's time to throw it away?*

REDISCOVER DESIRE

Every major transition in life requires rediscovering desire to some degree. Exhaustion, loss, heartbreak, disappointment, overwork, outgrowing situations and relationships, racism, sexism, there are so many reasons we lose desire. Fill in the blanks as many times as you can.

I feel desire and energy for _____
(*name an area or relationship*)

when I _____
(*what are you doing? Who are you with?*).

COMPLAINTS

What I complain about most includes... *You might need to ask friends, family, or co-workers for clues. Listen to what you say especially when you're frustrated or angry. Complaints are golden information; they often point to things we desire or need to change.*

REASONS TO BOTHER

I conceived my book *Why Bother? Discover the Desire for What's Next* when I told a friend going through a life meltdown, "Sometimes you have to fight for your life."

What's worth fighting for just because I want it, value it, love it? *Not because it gets you approval or money or helps others, although it might do all those things.*

SELF-KINDNESS

Every act of self-harshness stops the flow of life and creativity that brings you to what's next. Every time you judge yourself harshly and believe that's the truth about you, you move away from life, from getting your bother on, and fall back into the blah zone. You shut down your energy and you shut yourself off to life and learning. It's so obvious, but it's the biggest reason many of us don't have more of the lives we want.

It's not self-judgment that's the issue, that's just your brain doing its weird human thing. The issue is when you believe the story you are somehow bad or screwed up. Put that worn story back on the shelf and take down the story of generous honey-coated warming self-acceptance.

I was kind to myself recently when...

I'd like to be kinder to myself next time I... *Imagine a situation where you were self-punishing or cruel in your self-talk, then create a future scenario where you choose self-kindness.*

SELF-TALK

I lose some of my get-up-and-go when I think

about myself.
(*For me, it's comparing myself to others or replaying woulda-coulda-shoulda stories about my choices.*)

I get it back when I tell myself...

Sometimes what is draining your hope is how you're training your brain to focus on what you didn't do or think you did poorly rather than savoring what's good and what you enjoyed.

Good things that I experienced recently:

Saw

Tasted

Felt

Heard

Smelled

COMPANIONSHIP

Who have I accompanied from lost to found, from burned out to engaged, from grieving to starting a new life? Who have I sat with, listened to, and encouraged? *Include small gestures like a hug, a card, a text, or a chat at the mailbox. Celebrate how you connect.*

If I was going to ask someone to accompany me, who would I ask? What forms of support would I ask for? *Even if you aren't ready to ask, or don't know who to ask, name the support you want and what it would feel like. Let your imagination help you create a circle of belonging.*

REDISCOVER DESIRE

Draw a map of your bothering. Where did you start? Hint: it might be well in the past. What swamps and monsters have you overcome? What glorious adventures do you want in front of you? Where do you want to finish? Don't worry about drawing something pretty or that even makes sense. Instead create a hopeful future and a respectful past.

REASONS TO BOTHER

Write your bio of how you bother now and how you will bother in the future. Use the third person. Claim your power and vision in a grounded, strong way. Forget being demure.

HOW I BOTHER NOW

A few of the ways I am currently bothering, the situations where I do feel purpose, desire, meaning, commitment, alignment, juice, mojo include... *It can be easy to overlook or dismiss how you are bothering now so you might ask a few trusted individuals how they see you bothering, caring, where you are engaged or energized. Nothing is too small! Trust me when I say energy, desire, and life come in tiny rumblings and faint murmurs.*

GIFTS & STRENGTHS

What gifts and strengths do I value and how might I use them to get my bother on? *This is a prompt people tend to skip, because it feels like bragging or they aren't feeling good about themselves. You might prime yourself by asking a few friends or looking through magazines for pictures and words that remind you of your strengths.*

Doodle, collage, color, or write a poem or a paragraph about your gifts and strengths. You can be metaphorical, symbolic, or playful. Use your non-dominant hand and please don't be shy.

BODY & HEALTH

What, if anything, have I given up healing or improving around my relationship with my body or my health? *I have struggled with health issues most of my life and when I find myself wondering why bother to keep trying things,it's because I'm once again looking for a silver bullet, a magic quick fix, instead of aiming for gradual improvement and patient experimentation.*

COMPANIONSHIP & COMMUNITY CARE

Have you ever wondered if this is all there is? It's very normal to wonder. One way to recall all that is here, and does matter right now, is to show others they matter: From a card to a text to a donation to a high five to a good morning to a prayer. Connection gives meaning.

RESIST

How has the dominant culture made it harder for me to thrive? *This is not about being a victim, but instead about acknowledging that you live in a world where certain people are supported while many are left behind. By naming this, you remember it is not all up to you to get your bother on, it is a collective story, and you always have power.*

WHAT I KNOW NOW

Gentle reminder: your work is to settle down, to listen, to discern what matters to you now and to be brave enough to experience it without needing to know what it means or where it leads. To look for the daring bright beauty in your "why bother?" instead of the life-denying, heart-shrinking shrug. To believe in more, open the door to it, and invite it in.

Glance back over your responses to the various prompts in this section. What are you aware of now? What was most useful to you? (You don't have to wait until you do all the prompts, this is your journal, skip what you wish.) Make a few notes here of what you now know or are gently becoming aware of.

leave behind

The Leave Behind stage of getting your bother on is about letting go a little bit more of the past, so the present can have its turn. It's about forgiveness and letting go, especially letting go of the story that because you did or didn't do something, because something is no longer possible or has been taken from you, that your future can never be as satisfying or fulfilling.

What I needed to leave behind most in my "why bother?" times was my ancient battered story that I was a failure, that I failed at screenwriting, failed at being a self-help guru (thank god), failed at my first marriage, failed at novel writing, failed at parenting, failed at being a good friend, failed at living fully...

But each of those "failures" was in fact a tale of desire denied or truncated, *an opportunity to write a new story* that I turned away from, because I was too timid, too addicted to comfort, trying to be somebody important, or afraid of being poor.

I hadn't failed (and neither have you!). I needed to pause and embrace the knowledge that *something wasn't working*, hadn't worked, or was over, and now was the time to pause, settle down, build up my self-trust, and get to know my desires.

But what I often did instead was refuse to leave my past behind and begin again. I made my present and future self pay for my so-called failures. I refused to forgive myself and open my heart to the call of life.

You won't. You, too, have an opportunity to write a new story. It will be a different one than before, and it might not be the one you wanted or thought you would have but that doesn't mean it can't be wonderful in its own right. Let these next prompts open your heart and body to what's next.

REASONS TO BOTHER

Deciding you can't bother because your story didn't unfold the way you thought it would, or should, is self-cruelty to the highest degree. It's declaring, "Because my life doesn't look the way I think it should, I give up on my future." Or, "Because I can't do or have this particular thing, person, or way of living, my life has no meaning." Most of us do this to ourselves more than we realize but, thankfully, we can stop. It's a practice.

Divide the circle below into a pie chart that reflects how you want your energy to be divided up going forward. What slice of the pie will your past get from here on out? Your present? Your future? Label each section to remind youself how you want to divide your attention going forward.

HOW I BOTHER NOW

Note past events you regret or wish you could have handled differently. Then go back in time and recall what you actually knew and could do. Then zip forward: if that same event happened today, what do you know and what could you do now? Pay attention to how what you know and can do now is only possible because of what you did in the past.

Past Event	What I knew and could do then	What I know and can do now

WHY BOTHER

When I am completely honest with my beloved self, I know I don't want
to bother about _____ anymore and that's okay.
Fill in the blank as often you like. You might not be able to stop bothering
about certain things because of needing to make money, taking care of
others, or because you don't believe you can. Don't let that stop you for
naming the truth.

Out of 24 hours in a day, how many hours is my mind
a good place to hang out? A place of contentment,
kindness, self-acceptance, and general ease?

How many days a week?

What jerks and shoves my mind into being a place
I'm not comfortable in and at home?

What is one practice I've learned in the past that will help
me foster a kind mind? *Note it here and when you might
practice it again. Your attention is yours to direct*

CLEAR CLUTTER

Clearing clutter can be an awesome way to leave behind what no longer serves you and an incredibly freeing kind of self-care.

What is one space, no matter how small (a spot on a counter, one drawer, your texting inbox), that you could clear today to make space for what's next? *Even if you don't know what's next.*

Don't fill your newly cleared space with anything new for a few days. Instead, notice how having this space makes you feel.

Clutter makes it easier to forget that I might want to bother about... *Sometimes the clutter in our lives can provide a way to hide from our desires even as it makes us batty. Look around at your clutter. What might it be obscuring?*

EMOTIONAL IMMUNE SYSTEM

What if you're not afraid of change, success, or failure? What if you don't sabotage yourself? What if, in fact, you're simply brilliant at keeping yourself *defended*? What if you're incredibly skilled, like all humans, at self-protection and managing your emotional immune system?

The purpose of your emotional immune system is the same as your physical immune system: reject what threatens. Your emotional immune system's job is to keep you safe and to keep you away from anything that threatens to leave you exposed to failure, to a change in your identity, to humiliation, or to loss.

As Robert Kegan and Lisa Laskow Lahey note in *Immunity to Change*, "It is not change by itself that makes us uncomfortable... Rather, it is change that leaves us feeling defenseless before the dangers we 'know' to be present that cause us anxiety." You believe there are dangers present that will hurt you and that's why you don't do more of what you want.

Your brain and nervous system evolved to keep you safe, *not* to help you live a meaningful life. Knowing this, you can *learn how to make yourself feel safer* as you take action on what you desire. Your goal is not to get rid of your emotional immune system—that's impossible and, like your physical immune system, you need it to keep yourself safe—but rather to get familiar with how your emotional immune system hems you in, tricks you to stay safe in ways that are too small for you, and then to help it grow more robust and less easily triggered.

Your emotional immune system gives itself away when it diverts your desires into what Kegan and Laskow Lahey call "competing commitments." That's when you do the opposite of what you say you want to do. For example:

You start your novel and apply for a promotion that means working weekends.

You address your digestive issues and eat everything that makes you bloat and feel poorly.

You realize nothing will change for you without more sleep and then stay up until two in the morning watching police procedurals while arguing politics with trolls on Twitter.

You decide to delegate to your team so you can truly lead, and then you micromanage the next project more than ever.

All humans do this. Waste no time feeling embarrassed.

COMPETING COMMITMENTS

My current competing commitments might include...
*Sneak up on yourself. What might you be doing? Just possibly.
Think about this morning, last night, the last time you declared
you wanted to try something new, the last time you made a
promise to yourself you couldn't keep. It might help to keep this
page open and near you for a day or two.*

COMPETING COMMITMENTS

When you're reaching for or find yourself in the midst of a competing commitment, soothe yourself using:

   Self-touch: hand on your heart, rubbing your arms, patting your legs, giving yourself a hug.

   Exhaling longer than you inhale. Make an "mmm" sound or purse your lips slightly.

   Inhale to the count of 4, pause for the count of 4, exhale to the count of 4.

   Then speak to yourself with kindness. What would you say to a dear friend?

   Check in. "What am I telling myself about why I can't   ? What am I doing instead?" It can help to write this down because that helps executive function in your brain take over.

Here's the crucial bit: don't force yourself to do anything differently. Instead, hang out for another breath or three and *observe your emotional immune system in action*. Feel the pull to stay defended and label it, again in writing, if you can. But make no plans for action...yet.

Noticing, feeling, and making notes is much more powerful right now than anything else you can do.

When you notice your emotional immune system in action, note the situation, date, and what you did to soothe yourself. Not what you did to change, but to stay with yourself, on your own side.

Situation/Date	What I Did to Self-Soothe

RESIST

We are all heavily influenced by the cultures that surround
us. Often without knowing it, we absorb and believe stories
of what's not possible for us from our families, school
experiences, workplace, and the media.

Who told me
I can't?

What I say to that
person now

List the people, situations, settings, media depictions that make it hard for you to value yourself and your desires. Sometimes, you need to name your obstacles so you can remember you have the ability and power to move around them, over them, under them, or simply ignore them.

When your list is complete, scribble over everything you are no longer willing to let stop you. Leave the things you aren't ready to let go of yet or that you feel are true impediments you need help to overcome.

CHOOSING IS YOUR ART

How can I remind myself I always have a choice, I can always choose me, I can always stay on my own side? *Perhaps glue a picture of you feeling bold and strong, make up a rallying cry, or draw a symbol that reminds you "Yes I can," and "Yes I am" and add those here.*

REASONS TO BOTHER

Take yourself on a scavenger hunt around your home, your bookshelves, your work life, your digital life, or your photos. Search for signs of what you don't want to bother about and what you do want to bother about. Maybe unanswered emails give you an idea about commitments that you need to renegotiate, or a pile of unread books are an indicator of what you think you should learn or a sign of what you aren't making time for—it's up to you to interpret what you find. Read your life like a detective searching for clues. Note here what you discover.

FORGIVENESS

In third person, write down everything you haven't yet forgiven yourself for. Instead of I, use your name. Then reflect on what the cost is of not forgiving yourself for each item on your list. Again, as you do, use your name in the third person. Finally, in the third column, note any amends you're willing to offer to yourself or another person. For this part of the prompt, use the 1st person.

Forgive myself for	Cost	Amends

Choose one item from the list you just made and tell the story of something you are having a difficult time forgiving yourself for. Write your story in the third person. Instead of writing "me," write "he, she, or they," or use your name. Also imagine you are writing your story to someone who loves you utterly and unconditionally. This can be a real person, a spiritual figure, or a character from literature. You are not telling your story to justify why you did what you did, but instead to explain as factually as possible, giving needed context so your loving person can understand what happened. Tell only the parts of your story you feel comfortable telling.

Now, if you'd like, read your story aloud into the recorder on your phone and then replay it. As you listen, imagine it is not your story, but the story of someone you love and respect very much.

GIFTS & STRENGTHS

Where, when, and with whom might I hide my gifts and strengths? *Sometimes hiding is highly adaptive and smart, and it's good to know when and with whom you feel you must hide to be safe. You might be right, or you might be trapped by your emotional immune system.*

There's a growing body of science about mindset and how simple interventions can quickly change how we see ourselves and what's possible. For each left-hand column item, see if there is a reframe that makes sense to you and that you can believe is possible, even if it's a big stretch.

I can't *Learn to play the piano*	I want *To express myself through music*
I won't *Ever have my own business*	I might *Be curious about becoming a copywriter*
Not possible for me *Being truly healthy*	I wonder if *I could try finding someone to walk with*

REFRAMING YOUR MINDSET

When we believe we aren't good enough, we can't relax into life and let it reveal its marvels. Any thoughts you have of not being enough aren't factual and aren't personal. Try framing these thoughts as alien invaders because any feelings of not-enoughness are not organic to you but created by a culture that thrives on making people, especially women, people of color, differently-abled people, and LGBTQ+ folks feel less than. Take a moment to wonder: "What purpose does this alien invader serve? Who benefits?"

Draw or find representatives of these alien invaders.

WHY BOTHER?

What was never mine to bother about in the first place?
For example, earning your mother-in-law's approval, fitting
the dominant culture's picture of success, keeping your home
clean like your mom did, religious views you were raised with,
or caring about sports like your dad.

WHY BOTHER?

What might I need to truly walk away from, once and for all? *Again, it's okay if you aren't yet ready. If you are afraid or unsure what to name here, collect images that speak to this prompt.*

When I stop trying to control _____ ,
I have more energy and power to...

MONEY

Money will influence, shape, prevent, and enable how you bother. You can't ignore money; you can't wish it away or repeat prosperity affirmations until you pass out. You can't ignore that women earn less on the dollar than men, and that a Black woman on average will have to work twenty months to earn what a white man can earn in twelve.

But you also can't allow a lack of money to shut down the flow of your desires and to trap you in "why bother?" forever.

Money makes it difficult for me to...

And easy for me to...

What I believe about me and money includes ,
and I learned it when...

MONEY

To live the life I want, I would need to
with money.

CYNICISM

Activist and author Parker Palmer writes, "One of the most important qualities a person can have in our time—a person who wants to make this a better world—is the capacity to 'stand in the tragic gap' between corrosive cynicism and irrelevant idealism, between what is and could be. We need the inner strength to hold both the reality and our hope at the same time."

Imagine holding corrosive cynicism in one hand and irrelevant idealism in the other. How do they each feel? What temperature and weight do they have?

Which one do you like more? Which one is more comfortable or familiar?

Take three full breaths while bringing your hands up to either side of you.

Experiment with feeling yourself in the gap between these two ways of seeing. Relax your body.

Notice what is.

Notice what could be.

Let both exist here with you in the middle.

CYNICISM

Cynicism is perfectionism wrapped in self-protection disguised as world-weary experience. It's saying, "I'd rather disappoint myself now than be disappointed later."

Because life is about opening my heart and risking connection and full expression, I'm ready to own my wholeness and power by...

You may veer into the swampland of cynicism and feel like giving up because you've bothered so much, because you've hoped and prayed and worked your butt off, and it either hasn't seemed to be effective or you've burned out.

What makes me feel defeated, like I can't do enough for others or the planet?

CYNICISM

Research shows that if you judge your efforts to help as ineffective or insufficient, you will quit doing much of anything. Or, if you do continue to give and help, you will not reap the psychological benefits of connecting with a sense of purpose, which can lead to burnout.

Where might my assessment of not doing enough be getting in my way of engaging in and benefiting from how I care for the world?

What adjustments, if any, would I like to make in how I serve? What changes would I like to make in how I perceive the efficacy of what I do? How might conditions of enoughness help?

BODY & HEALTH

What stories and beliefs about my health make it hard for me to bother the way I might like? *These stories and beliefs may be well rooted in experiences and diagnoses, yet science continues to learn how powerful our minds are in determining how we feel, including pain.*

WHAT I KNOW NOW

You are about to receive a gift. A gift that will help you remember, with all your body and heart, how having more, loving more, enjoying more, and creating more is not only possible, but is already happening.

A gift that can only be given to you because you have created room for it by leaving behind what no longer serves you or can be yours.

By letting go, what comes to you?

Close your eyes and let this gift become real to you. Receive. Describe your gift.

ease in

The Ease In stage of getting your bother on is all about getting the energy to follow your desires and about giving yourself the necessary space and freedom for true and lasting transformation. This section is where you fine-tune your self-care so you can bother. Where you pay close attention to the inklings and stirrings of what pulls you into the flow of life, and nurture these with curiosity and attention.

But if you are anything like me, you may crave certainty and surety. You want to know NOW that everything will work out for the best. That's cool. Let whatever your mind demands be fine while you keep putting your attention on wonder, self-kindness, self-compassionate grit, and deeper engagement.

Remind yourself there is no clear finish line you need to reach, no marching band waiting for you. Instead, there is a slow-growing sense of rightness, purpose, aliveness, wonderment, enthusiasm, and satisfaction.

And that sounds way better than a marching band to me.

REASONS TO BOTHER

Make a handprint here like ancient people did on cave walls. Declare you matter to yourself.

SELF-KINDNESS

Read this invocation aloud. It's one I use at the Oasis, my online community, to help us settle and feel your essential goodness.

I am here and welcome just as I am.
No matter what, I trust this being, this body, this heart.
No matter what, I accept myself as I am.
No matter what, I trust my essential goodness.
No matter what, it is safe to know and honor my desires.

Because I am welcome just as I am...

When I trust my body, I discover... *If you can, let your body answer. Try using your non-dominant hand.*

SELF-KINDNESS

My essential goodness feels like... *It might be lovely to find a picture of you that reminds you of how you embody your essential goodness and add it here.*

It's safe to desire... *If it doesn't feel safe yet, what you would like to be safe to desire?*

ANGER

Starting at a young age, girls are often taught that it's not acceptable to feel anger or to express it. Over time, we may learn to doubt what we see, what we feel, what we value, and that what we want matters. Not owning or knowing our anger undermines our agency and our self-trust.

I'm angry about...

I've been angry about
for a long time.

ANGER

Suppressing your anger can teach you to be a pessimist, resigned to powerlessness, and can make you turn your rage on yourself instead of on the systems that need to change. It can prevent you from taking constructive, righteous action.

What five actions is my anger pointing me toward taking?

1

2

3

4

5

There's a component of getting your bother on that's easy to overlook but is, in fact, indispensable: self-care. These are the basic things you need in place to pursue a fulfilling life. Without these basics, it's far easier to fall into and stay stuck in the yucky sticky blah kind of "why bother?".

But these basics aren't sexy or easy to remember, so they can fall by the wayside and create a feeling of lassitude and pointlessness all by themselves. We become so accustomed to doing without or feeling like crap, we give up, and that giving up spreads to our whole life. Life will never be perfect, but it also shouldn't always be lived at a constant deficit.

Here are some of examples from readers (note: none of these are "should" or are right, they are only common examples of what people have found essential for *themselves*):

In bed by 9:30 with devices off

Keep the phone off on Sunday and out of my bedroom at night

Exercise in some way for 15 minutes

Meditate for 10 minutes

Read scripture

Freewriting for 5 minutes about my feelings

Doing anything creative on the weekend

Eating something fresh

Connecting with friends and my sister

Putting my hands in dirt

Making something new and exciting for a meal

Getting out into nature, watching birds, listening, looking closely

The following pages contain prompts to help you name your minimums.

SELF-CARE

What helps me stay on my own side and treat myself with kindness includes... *For example, kind self-talk, coaching or therapy, alone time, journaling.*

I get out of whack if I have or do too much... or if I have too little of... *Too much processed food, too much wine, too little nature, too little fun.*

It's easy for me to judge myself for needing... *Time to create, beauty, a clutter-free kitchen.*

I get cranky when I don't or can't...
Connect with someone who understands me, volunteer, pray.

SELF-CARE

I could live without _____, but it
wouldn't be fun. *Think of people, art forms, nature...*

If I'm really honest, what my body needs is...
Time to hear myself think and feel my feelings.

My friend Anna Guest-Jelley, who created Curvy Yoga, adjusts her self-care seasonally. For example, she focuses on allergy self-care in early spring and uses a light box in the winter.

Seasonal adjustments I would love to make in my self-care… *It's okay if you can't. This is not about goals but about knowing what you need, so you can get it more of the time. Nobody is interested in, or trying for, perfect self-care—so boring.*

SELF-CARE

What everybody tells me I should do for self-care, but I don't and I won't... *Skip email first thing in the morning, meditate, do morning pages.*

Taking care of yourself so you can get your bother on more and more of the time is always based on your choice and preferences. If something feels like self-violence or self-improvement, run away. If you aren't ready for something, stop pushing. Self-care is never one size fits all.

SELF-CARE

Look back over what you wrote in the last few pages and compile your own list of your current minimums. Return here often to read over, change, and add to your list.

When you check back here, ask yourself, "When is the last time I . . .?" Watch out for your emotional immune system pulling the curtain over your needs by insisting you're just fine, thank you very much. Even the most basic kind of self-care can bring up feelings of selfishness, vulnerability, a mistrust of pleasure, and lack of time. This is not about goals, self-improvement, or forcing yourself. It's about coming back to yourself.

My List

SHADOW COMFORTS & TIME MONSTERS

"Shadow comforts" is a term I coined when writing my first book, The Woman's Comfort Book, in the early '90s. It's anything you do in the name of self-care but instead of recharging you or helping you stay engaged with life, shadow comforts leave you feeling worse about yourself or leave you numb. Not because of what you do, but why you do it and how it makes you feel.

Something can be a nourishing comfort one day and shadow comfort the next. For example, watching an episode of your favorite show to wind down vs. watching an episode (or 5) to numb out your anger at your partner.

A concept related to shadow comforts is time monsters. Time monsters are things you need to do like clean the bathroom, answer email, cook dinner, but you let these activities gobble up the time you could spend on other activities you desire but are afraid of like writing, starting a side-hustle, dating.

What are some of my favorite shadow comforts these days?

For more thoughts on shadow comforts and time monsters, check out Why Bother? Discover the Desire for What's Next. *You can order a copy and pick up your thank you gifts here: jenniferlouden.com/why-bother*

Give your shadow comforts and time monsters a name, a texture, a color. What famous person do they remind you of? Doodle or collage about them here. It will give you a sense of choice and agency, and it might make you laugh.

SHADOW COMFORTS & TIME MONSTERS

My favorite time monsters include... *Remember you need to do these things, but you may be doing them first, making them more complex, or giving them more time than necessary.*

You might find it helpful to look back at your Competing Commitments from page 37 and see if you listed any Shadow Comforts or Time Monsters there.

My shadow comforts often defend me from...
What do they keep you from feeling, doing, trusting, risking?

My time monsters often keep me from...

BODY & HEALTH

One way I've been wanting to ease in to
cherishing my body and health is...

And that could look like...

COMPANIONSHIP & COMMUNITY CARE

Is there any situation or relationship where you feel like you don't belong? Name those.

If you were to look at each of these as an opportunity to help someone else belong or feel included, what comes to mind to try?

SELF-COMPASSIONATE GRIT

Self-compassionate grit invites you to treat yourself with the same love and care you do others, while you stay engaged and in action on what you care about. Self-compassionate grit offers an alternative to numbing out and shadow comforts (which I used to turn to in the name of self-compassion): "I can't handle anymore today, I have to go watch *Schitt's Creek* and eat Coconut Bliss," or grinding yourself into a pile of rubble of overwork and high expectations.

Self-compassionate grit is gentle, firm determination married to self-kindness. It's saying to yourself, "Get off the couch, honey, you can do it," without adding, "get to it now, you lazy sod or everything will fall apart." You take action while staying on your own side.

Self-compassionate grit steadies you. It gives you earplugs of love when the self-protective whispers of your emotional immune system try to convince you to go back, give up, stop.

You may naturally approach life this way. Notice if you sometimes swing toward so much self-compassion that you give up on your desires or convince yourself you can't (this is not true self-compassion), or you force yourself to hurry, scurry even when you need a rest, a pee break, or time to settle.

Self-compassionate grit comes
easily for me when...

But not so easily when....

If self-compassionate grit were a character from a favorite book or movie, she would be...

WONDER

Wonder opens the door to desire. It brings back freshness. It lives beyond the known and entices you toward a new way of seeing, feeling, and living. Wonder is the inspiration behind bothering again, and it's a powerful way to ease in to what's next.

Wonder:

Does not analyze, fix, or prescribe.

Refuses to know.

Declines to figure anything out.

Sees beyond frozen feelings of inevitability.

Communicates in flashes, images, shivers, "livewire" dreams, slivers of ideas, or a line from a song you can't get out of your head.

Flirts with grace and sleeps with mystery.

Is never less than present.

Does not recognize difficulty as a problem but as a summons.

Doesn't care who you think you are.

Inveigles you to remember life is, by its very nature, creative.

Sweeps fatalism, cynicism, pessimism, parochialism, and all otherisms away.

Disturbs you; pokes you awake at three in the morning; causes you to try things, say things, and think things that make your friends or your kids say, "Who are you?"

Often communicates in questions.

Doesn't care where it takes you, only that it does.

What does wonder mean to me?
Open me to? Remind me of?

WONDER

Wonder's job is to breathe you to life. Stroll somewhere familiar and notice what you haven't noticed before. See if you can use all your senses, not just sight (Yes, even taste.). Depict what you experience using wonder as your muse.

Collect images that fill you with wonder here.

WONDER

What do you keep spurning? Turning your back on? Saying no way, that's too weird or has no clear purpose. Maybe making Grandma's cookie recipe. Finding your cousin and asking what she remembers about that summer. Writing about your sister's illness. The point is to pay attention. Instead of:

"I don't eat sugar, why make her cookie recipe?"

"I haven't talked to Nila Jo since we were twelve, and I wouldn't even know what to ask her."

"It'll be too painful to write about Sue being sick; I can't go there."

Can you ask, "I wonder..."

I have been shrugging off or denying _____,
and if I didn't, I would...

SELF-TRUST

Self-trust starts with paying attention to what you're feeling, sensing, and noticing, rather than reflexively looking outside yourself for guidance. Self-trust is the habit of asking yourself, "What do I know?" and "What do I want?" and then doing research. It's about giving yourself time to feel your way into your next simple step. It's about having faith in your own experiences.

12 things I trust about myself:

1

2

3

4

5

6

7

8

9

10

11

12

SELF-TRUST

12 things I trust about people I love:

1

2

3

4

5

6

7

8

9

10

11

12

12 things about me people I love trust:
(Ask only people you love and trust,
people whose opinion you value.)

SELF-TRUST

Think about something that is unclear, confusing, or that you are unsure how to do. Just one thing please. List everything you trust about yourself to handle this situation with love, care, and dignity (which is different than handling it perfectly and getting the right outcome).

Paying attention to when you live your values strengthens your self-trust. *Listed below are a handful to get you thinking.*

Authenticity	Faith	Inclusion	Passion	Simplicity
Beauty	Fairness	Kindness	Pleasure	Success
Boldness	Friendship	Justice	Positivity	Thankfulness
Challenge	Family	Learning	Responsibility	Wisdom
Curiosity	Growth	Love	Self-Respect	Wealth
Community	Humor	Mindfulness	Service	

I live my values when...

SELF-TRUST

I'd like to live my values more often by...

If I didn't need to be   ,

then I could trust myself to...

HABITS & ROUTINES

When do I choose comfort over aliveness?
How exactly do I do that? When is it okay with me,
even helpful, and when does it feel stale?

If I was going to design another way to support my emotional immune system in keeping me safe while stretching—perhaps a new habit or routine that would allow me a little wiggle room to try one new thing—what might I design?

HABITS & ROUTINES

One way to open your imagination to new ways of supporting what's next is to mess with your current habits in silly ways that intrigue you to consider new possibilities. For example:

Sleep on the opposite side of the bed.

Brush your teeth with your other hand.

Share a meal in silence, using hand gestures and anything else you like, except words, to have a conversation.

Order something new on the menu at your favorite restaurant.

Drive a different route to work or to do your errands.

Talk to someone you would normally avoid or be shy around.

Rearrange the furniture in the room you use the most.

Use whatever you always save for later or special occasions.

Get dressed with your eyes closed.

Wear makeup if you never do; wear no makeup if you always do.

Write your to-do list with your non-dominant hand.

Dance first thing in the morning. Crank up the sound (you can use headphones if need be).

Recite poetry in the shower.

What did you try?

I've gotten in the habit of   ,
and while I'm not ready to change my behavior yet, I'm curious
how this habit drains me and makes it hard for me to...

GATHER STORIES

Who do I think bothers in a way that satisfies and delights them? *Name people you know, neighbors, people you admire, celebrities, or fictional characters.*

What's your evidence that the people you listed opposite bother in a way that satisfies and delights them? Is it what they create? Their relationships? Their energy? Their philanthropy? This is total projection, but what you fantasize about can offer clues to how and what you want to bother about.

settle

The Settle stage of getting your bother on is about finding the stillness that makes everything else possible. It's about calming your nervous system and mind so you can hear what's calling you and trust yourself enough to explore it.

What if the only hurdle in the way of getting your bother on and being in love with life is stopping? Resting? Rooting down into being? *Settling?*

If there is one reason people don't find their way to being fulfilled, to living the deeper life they crave, it is because they refuse to settle.

Settling is a complete stop of hectic, grasping, breathless, desperate doing. It's stepping out of the digital hurly-burly, the family drama, the inner drama; stepping away from figuring things out, from self-improvement, from ambition, and even from learning new things. For example, every time a colleague of mine got close to figuring out what she really wanted, she signed up for another course or certification, instead of trusting what she already knew.

Settling takes intention and focus but not effort. It is not to be confused with settling for less, which is what we do when we don't know why we bother.

It can be very unsettling to settle in with yourself, both because you might have become accustomed to constantly doing or being distracted and because when you don't have anything to do to distract your mind, you hear and feel it doing its thing and that can be wild to witness. Settling down is *not* about having a blank mind: that's impossible. Nor is it about sitting still. Some of us find that makes us far more anxious and unsettled.

It's about finding your way to be, to dwell in yourself, to come back into your body and spiritual gravity, and let go of *doing as proof you matter*. Settling down signals that you decline to jack yourself up and always live in reaction mode.

When you settle, you come into immediate contact with one of the most potent forces for change: the grounding grace of inner stillness. It's always inside you, waiting to receive you.

Can you feel it here, right now?

BEING

I sometimes find it delicious to just be, to settle, to rest because... *If you aren't sure you do find it delicious, can you imagine how it could be? Ask your body to give you a hint.*

COMPLAINTS

I find it useful to blame

for why I can't settle down. *This might sound harsh, but sometimes you have to see how you use others to stop yourself and where you might need better boundaries.*

Perhaps look back at page 4 at your best memories of bothering and see if that brings to mind related times of settling down that felt great.

GET YOUR BOTHER ON: SETTLE **106**

GATHER STORIES

Recall a time when you were more present and more easily absorbed by your activities and the world. What was different? What choices did you make that might have been different? What beliefs or thoughts do you remember about what you were doing or not doing?

RESIST

I think settling down has to look like _____,
but I don't like that so I... *Name how you've been sold or
told to settle.*

I made you a yoga nidra inspired audio. It's waiting to soothe you at *jenniferlouden.com/whybother*

GET YOUR BOTHER ON: SETTLE **108**

SIMPLE WAYS TO FOSTER BEING & INNER STILLNESS

Leave your phone at home. Look for what you would never notice. Settle while you stand in line.

Turn off news alerts, email program alerts, social media alerts, and text message alerts.

Take a walk or run in silence.

Read a poem aloud slowly. Try the anthologies *Staying Alive* edited by Neil Astley or *Poetry of Presence* edited by Phyllis Cold-Dai and Ruby R. Wilson.

Memorize a poem.

Sketch something without taking your eyes off what you're sketching.

Let your body dance.

Try yoga nidra. Google the term; you can find lots of free audios to try.

Imagine you find a secret message about how you can settle down in a way that makes your soul sing. What would it say?

WHY BOTHER?

It's very common to avoid settling down because of childhood messages, societal norms, fears you can't handle being with yourself, the habit of being ultra-productive, and a nervous system that's gotten habituated to being jacked up.

I'm wary of settling down because...

THIS, TOO, BELONGS

You need not sprint away from your grief, your sadness, your insecurities, your heartbreaks, your disappointments, or any fears of being seen. Instead, welcome them with "this, too, belongs" and allow what feels like the block to become the doorway.

Welcome the excuses—it's too hard, there is no time, it's too painful, I don't know how, it's overwhelming—too. Everything can be welcomed.

Then life can enter and love you awake. Then your self-trust grows stronger as you realize you can feel and see your inner life; nothing is too ugly.

Say hello to what's here now so you can hear what wants to emerge next.

Put your hand on your heart and welcome yourself here.

Greet all the feelings.

The thoughts.

Welcome all the sensations.

If something emerges that needs to be done, make a note and a clear promise to yourself later. Say I'm sorry to my sister, pay the bill, or have the hard conversation with my spouse.

Then come back to welcoming.

Remember to breathe.

Nowhere else to be, nothing else to do.

BEING

I've treasured this quotation from *The Heroine's Journey* by Maureen Murdock for thirty years: "When a woman stops doing, she must learn how to simply be. Being is not a luxury; it is a discipline. The heroine must listen carefully to her true inner voice. That means silencing the other voices anxious to tell her what to do. She must be willing to hold the tension until the new form emerges. Anything less aborts growth, denies change, and reverses transformation. Being takes courage and demands sacrifice."

Whose voices will I silence so I can simply be?
It's not rude or selfish; it's essential.

HABITS & ROUTINES

It can be easy to confuse having time to yourself with settling down.
You aren't crazy busy, yet you aren't present. The day goes by in starts and
stops, bits and drabs, and you feel scattered. If this feels familiar, notice in
the moment what you tell yourself about why you have to keep doing or
jump up or have to finish before... Record what you notice here.

It's just easier if I ...

First, I have to...

I'm honestly the only one who can...

If I don't, _____ will probably happen and then...

SELF-TRUST

The messages I've received about resting, being quiet, listening deeply from others... *Positive, negative, supportive, judgmental, what comes to mind?*

What do you want to keep as your truth?

WHAT MY ATTENTION DID TODAY

Capture in doodles, splotches of color, shapes, however you like, what your attention felt like today. What was its quality? How fast or slow? What did it focus on?

HABITS & ROUTINES

Setting up good conditions to settle down trains your brain and body to make the transition more easily and quickly. Same comfy chair, listening to a particular playlist, a comforting blanket or shawl, an eye pillow, hot tea or the same glass for your water are all possibilities.

It's also useful to be able to settle down when we are out in the world, doing errands, at the office or at school, waiting for our kids or grandkids to be done with a lesson or sports, or commuting. You might put together a simple "on-the-go" settle down kit.

Sometimes we think we shouldn't need any help, or we resist making ourselves a priority by planning ahead and giving ourselves support. We insist we be tough or do it all alone. But why make it more difficult than it need be? Why not treat yourself with love?

What is one small step I could take today to create better conditions to settle down?

MINI TRANSITIONS

At the Oasis we regularly check in with our mini transitions: the moments in our day and our week when something is finished or completed, but the next thing hasn't started yet or isn't clear. Mini transitions include going to work, coming home, before making dinner, after a meeting, when you finish a task or when you are tired and need a break.

Mini transitions are ripe opportunities to settle down and tune into your desires. And they are also ripe moments to get snagged by time monsters or shadow comforts, because we are accustomed to doing, and an object in motion stays in motion.

Mini transitions in my day and week:

Circle two or three that might be a tempting moment to pause and settle

BODY & HEALTH

When I settle down, my body feels like _____ ,
and it tells me it wants...

WHAT I NOW KNOW

Settling down is a learned skill. We're social creatures, we have complex lives to tend to, and being quiet with ourselves often takes effort. Nevertheless, who is going to determine your future—Netflix, your boss, your pet, social media, your to-do list, or your deeper desires, values, aspirations, or the full and awakened life calling to you? Settling down is an act of soul resistance, and your life depends on it.

What will never become clear, never grow roots and become real, or never feel truly possible to me if I don't settle?

desire

The Desire stage is the heart of the *get your bother on* approach. This section will help you make friends with the often misunderstood quality and energy of desire, replace substitute desires, soften old fears of desire, and discern between grasping and growing. I've been trying to understand desire for decades which, come to think of it, is probably the wrong approach! Desire is life, energy, and inspiration, not something to be pinned down. I'm still learning that without desire, there is no life, and the purpose of desire is to draw us forward into living, into what captivates us; not to help us attain a particular career, creative goal, get paid more, or even to stay married or find lasting love.

Desire is a fraught word with a vast history, because our desires have been used against us for millennium. Most anyone who doesn't fit the norm, or anyone who needs to be disenfranchised to feed the economic machine, has had their desires used against them, denied, or snatched away. Desire has been used as an excuse to kill us, imprison us, stigmatize us, and shut us up. We've been told our desires are selfish, untoward, unladylike (that one makes me so furious), greedy, stupid, impossible, not for people like us, meaningless, irresponsible, pointless because won't earn any money (or a lot of it), and on and on.

This is precisely why I use the word: to reclaim its history and power. Desire is a one-word feminist manifesto. Desire has guts. It stands for something. It is the heart of sovereignty, the key to being the ruler of your own life, which is essential for getting your bother on. To be the agent of your own life, you must be able to want. Not to grasp, not to grind, not to identify with your desires, not to tie your identity and well-being to specific outcomes, but to let yourself open to the energy of life.

To let yourself become alive with desire.

DEFINE FOR YOURSELF

Is there another word or words you feel more comfortable using other than desire? Search through the thesaurus and list the words you find that you like more.

Look your words up. I like to use Onelook.com, because it has so many dictionaries linked in one place. What do you learn about your words? Do these words have the chops you need to get your bother on?

HOW I BOTHER NOW

Desire can feel like it has to be a big deal about something grandiose, special, or lasting. It has to change the world or earn you fame or fortune. When really desire is life saying, "Try this. Does this bring you alive? What about this? Do you want more? Less?" Desire is energy arising. What if it were that simple?

What do I most desire to experience today?

SKIP SELF-IMPROVEMENT

When does your desire get squelched by shoulds or trying to be more virtuous, productive, or healthy? I'm not saying eating ice cream for breakfast every day is a deep desire, but rather that always saying no to your little desires because "I shouldn't" stops you from knowing and trusting yourself to explore bigger desires.

If I find myself thinking, "I shouldn't" or "I'm being bad," how might I relax and truly enjoy whatever it is I'm wanting? How can I make that okay? *And if you can't or it doesn't feel safe, that's okay too.*

What would it feel like if I accepted that I'm fine just as I am right now? *Perhaps add colors or images to the page to depict how that feels or how you want it to feel.*

SKIP SELF-IMPROVEMENT

Related to squelching or judging your small desires is confusing desire with self-improvement, with changing something about yourself so you can finally enjoy life.

Because I don't need to wait to enjoy my life and there is nothing "wrong" with me, today I desire...

BEING & DESIRE

When I allow myself to slow down and settle,
I find myself desiring...

CHOOSING IS YOUR ART

To have a healthy relationship with desire, you remember your life belongs to you and that you have the right to live your life the way you wish. To desire is to know and exercise your right to choose.

But sometimes we are afraid to choose because we have made missteps in the past, we've fallen into the death trap of perfectionism, someone has us hurt badly, or we are tired of being disappointed. Yet to not choose is to stay stuck in why bother. It is to miss out on life.

I say no to

I say yes to

If choosing is not about getting it right or avoiding disappointment but about opening to life, I find myself wanting to choose...

LOSS OF DESIRE

Loss of desire, mojo, clarity, direction, or purpose is normal. Your job is to keep normalizing it while never believing it's permanent or "all you deserve" or "the best my life can ever be."

Desire and purpose go missing for many reasons: because you're afraid to go for what you want; because you learned from the dominant culture to constantly hate on yourself; because you age out of a desire; because you completed something and you don't know what's next yet; because something is taken from you; because you've learned what you need to learn and it's time to move on; because you're exhausted; because you've stayed too long in a job or relationship or identity to be safe or take care of others; because you've put everyone else first forever; because you've never had the agency or resources to ask, "What do I want?"

How, where, and when did I lose my desire?

Sometimes desire involves reclaiming what has been lost, pushed aside, or put off because you had to make a living, take care of kids or parents, recover from an illness. Whatever the reasons something vital and important went underground.

Desires I needed to put aside in the past are...

Record your desires then come back in a few days and cross out or rewrite anything that no longer truly beckons to you. Part of having a good relationship with desire is allowing what you want to change as you grow and age.

REASONS TO BOTHER

Some desires do not go missing. Some desires we hang onto, believe in, or stay in relationship with easier than others. They bring us back to life when we honor them in some way.

The desires I've held on to, sometimes with ease, sometimes with fierce devotion include...

FEAR OF DESIRE

Pam, a longtime member of the Oasis, wrote me a beautiful letter when I was writing *Why Bother?* about why she is afraid to desire: "Expressing a desire or even a true physical need was dangerous when I was a child. Expressing a desire was to draw attention to myself . . . Better to be silent and forgotten. I learned never to express desire, and this grew into never even admitting desire to myself, lest I slip up and reveal it to someone else."

The reasons I can't have more of what I desire include...

Now choose one story from your list. Imagine it is across the room from you on a screen. Notice that this is the past. It is no longer true. Allow the scene and screen to dissolve completely.

FEAR OF DESIRE

I have protected myself from knowing or acting on
my desires, because I believed...

The desires I have ignored more than once...

REDISCOVER DESIRE

A friend decided to try and get pregnant in her mid-40s after a long-term relationship ended with a man who never wanted children and she reckoned with how much she did, and always had. She said, "I just needed to let myself want what I wanted and try for what my heart desired. I'd done such a good job, all those years with L., of making peace with not being able to have or even try for something that my heart wanted. I think it shut off a lot of other things... the deepest, most creative part of me got the message that what I desired was inappropriate or unnecessary. So even if no baby comes from this, by telling my family and friends, 'This is something I want, for no reason other than I want it,' I'm healing something."

Something I want, for no reason other than I want it...

What might heal by letting myself want
without knowing if I'll achieve it or fulfill it?

In *The Radiance Sutras*, Lorin Roche writes, "The ultimate source of desire is the soul's impulse to express itself in the world." Gather images, magazine pictures, symbols, phrases that depict your soul's impulse to express itself. Trust your soul to show you.

REDISCOVER DESIRE

When I refuse to judge myself for what I desire,
I find I want...

And I don't want...

What do I do, how do I react, when I want
something, but I can't have it?

BODY & HEALTH

What does my body keep insisting it wants, or wants to try, even if my mind says there is no point or "been there, tried that"?

DESIRE MANTRAS

Sweet things to tell yourself when you feel desire is impossible or scary.

There is more life to come.

It is safe to desire. I'm an adult, and I make it safe.

I can experience more—more aliveness, more connection, more creativity—starting now. It's here *now*. I don't have to wait or ask for permission.

I can rest in the gap between desire and satisfaction.

Life is not a problem to be solved.

I take responsibility for my desires.

I no longer need to make myself small or hide from what I want in order to protect others.

It is not about getting it right; it is about moving forward from what I feel and know now.

I have permission to live my life for my purposes.

This is my life. I am so lucky to be here for this. For all of it.

Anything you would add?

WONDER & DESIRE

If I didn't have to be successful (whatever that means to you), I might be curious about...

COMPANIONSHIP & COMMUNITY CARE

Desire shared is desire squared. What are 10 ways I could share a desire with someone, today or in the future?

COMPANIONSHIP & COMMUNITY CARE

How could sharing my desires with people, or communities I care about, inspire others to claim their desires?

RESIST

Forget asking permission or apologizing excessively.
You are a sovereign being and this is your life. Of course, you
may want and need to coordinate your actions with others,
your partner, co-workers, kids, but you do not ask permission
or say "I'm sorry" for wanting.

I will never again ask permission to....

I will never again apologize for...

SUBSTITUTE DESIRES

Why do you settle for substitutes for what you really want?
Because of your emotional immune system. Because life can
be complex and hard. Because desire can feel too risky.
Because the world sells desire as a glossy state of ideal feeling,
as goddess-infused crystal-encrusted self-care, as rainbow-
hued self-fulfillment and glowing happiness. Because you might
not have the energy to own a desire... yet.

My current favorite substitute desires are _____,
because they allow me to...

I can't have _____ , because...

.

So instead, I give myself...

SUBSTITUTE DESIRES

But what I might really want is... *Take what you wrote on that last page and see if it reveals a hidden or deferred desire. Sometimes there is hidden gold in what you are choosing instead.*

TRANSFORMING SUBSTITUTE DESIRES, SHADOW COMFORTS, TIME MONSTERS

How do you transform substitute desires, shadow comforts and time monsters into something more nourishing and life-giving? You tap into your desire!

The next time you reach for what could be a shadow comfort, time monster, or substitute desire, pause. You can have whatever you're reaching for—promise yourself that and be sure you mean it—but why not be sure it's what you truly want?

Ask yourself: **Is this what I want?** If the answer is yes, then enjoy thoroughly or focus completely. If you aren't sure, have what you've already chosen while noticing if you are enjoying yourself or fully engrossed?

If there is something else I want more, even though I can't have it, can I let myself know what it is? You can't discover what you want or might want if you immediately cut off your longings with a harsh, "but I can't have it, so there's no point in wanting it." You have no idea where your desire might lead you. Breathe into the sensation of wanting, of longing, and of not knowing how or if your wanting will be fulfilled. Invite wonder in to be your companion. This moment of not knowing how, when, or if is often exactly where your "why bother?" is regenerated.

If you find yourself saying, "I have to first do everything on my list, and then I can do what I want," **swap the order** and, for one day or one hour or ten minutes, do what you want first.

WONDER & DESIRE

Play with bringing wonder and desire together. As in "I wonder what it would be like to swap apartments with somebody in Istanbul," or "I wonder how people start a boot manufacturing business?"

I wonder what...

I wonder if...

I wonder how...

CHOOSING IS YOUR ART

What I want, and I am allowing, is...

What I want, and I am not allowing, is...

What I do *not* want, and I am allowing, is...

What I do *not* want, and I am not allowing, is...

REDISCOVER DESIRE

What continues to beckon to your heart and beguile your mind even though you keep trying to be done with it or declare it impossible?

Place an object across the room that represents something you really want; anything from having more energy, to gaining clarity about your next career move, to writing a book, to falling in love.

Describe, in writing, where you are right now and your current reality with this desire. What is your current energy level? What ideas and actions are you trying? What are you doing? Make a note.

Stand up. Feel your current reality. Not your story about it—how things won't ever change or your big plans for the perfect success—but the physical posture, breathing, muscle tone, facial expression of your current reality.

Take one step toward what you want represented by the object you choose...

Notice what happens to your body. Your thoughts. Your emotions.

When you get to what you want, do your body, your thoughts, your emotions need to shift to make room for your desire?

What would support you in being here, feeling safe here?

What happened when you were moving toward what you desire? What about when you got there? What is happening for you now?

SELF-TRUST

Because I can only live in the present,
and because I am safe to pursue my desires,
I am ready to explore....

I will put my desires
first this week by...

WHAT I KNOW NOW

Look back over what you've written in this journal, over weeks, months, even years.

What desires keep showing up? What desires make your breath catch, your heart beat faster? What desires make you feel more you? Depict them here.

become by doing

The become by doing stage of getting your bother on is about experimenting with ways to anchor your desires in the here and now. It is about taking action and seeing how that action changes you.

Here are three truisms I offer my students and clients in this stage. The first is to remember you become the person who can do the thing you want to do by doing it. You aren't that person yet and the only way to become that person is to take action on what you want. You grow only through the messy uncertainty of doing. There is no life hack, no degree, no certification, nothing that can change this truth. No matter what, you still have to get going and let the doing change you.

The second is beware making a plan. When you are wondering and wandering, your emotional immune system may heckle and chide you to make a fancy complicated plan but any plan you make now will be too small for who you're becoming. There's a world of difference between trying things out and making a plan that gives you the false comfort of certainty. You need more time to explore and change first.

The third and final truism is mood follows action; action changes mood. Don't wait to be in the mood to take action. Let action inspire more action. This is surprisingly easy to forget and always powerful to enact.

This next section of this journal is focused on concrete experimentation and data gathering; opening yourself even more to caring and learning through doing but not so much as a way to find clarity. Clarity is a beautiful thing, but sometimes we latch on to it too soon as a way to defend ourselves from becoming bigger, brighter, and more alive.

And that's what getting your bother on is all about! It's happening. Please keep trusting and nurturing it.

REDISCOVER DESIRE

To take more consistent skillful action on what you want, it helps to learn to accept your current situation at the same time you allow the energy of what you desire to inspire you. I call this relaxing in the gap, the gap being that almost ever-present space between what you can do now and what you want to do, between where you are and where you want to be.

Try to stick to just the facts under the "Current Situation" column and under "What I Desire" focus more on concrete actions you can take vs. ideal outcomes you dream of.

Current Situation   What I Desire

Responding to desire means you listen to how desire is calling you rather than asking, "Do I feel like it?" If we let our moods dictate our lives, we get lost in our stories and feelings, or rely solely on effort and willpower to move forward, which is exhausting. Moods are as changeable as the weather and not reliable criteria to base your life on.

Each time you do what you want, don't do what you don't want to do, or you check in with yourself, you strengthen the understanding that you are not your mood, not your thoughts, not your stories, not how your brain tries to keep you safe. You have a choice, even if you are depressed and anxious, in pain, or overwhelmed.

Desire says, "Let's learn about racial injustice," or "Let's work in the garden," and your mood says, "When I feel like it." In that moment, lean on self-compassionate grit on page 82 to move forward.

Try out one of these questions when you feel like not budging or like you must will your life to change:

What could be my next simple step?

Who could I ask for help?

What would be enough for today?

What do I need to stop and learn?

Where am I hurrying and being unrealistic?

Use one or more of these questions to get into action on one desire, no matter how small or wispy, right now.

How did that feel?

SIGNATURE THEMES

I've long been intrigued by the idea that everyone has "signature themes"—particular ideas, interests, passions, or issues that keep returning, wanting to be explored and worked with. It's not what form these themes take that matters, but that they won't leave you alone, that they demand attention, that they inveigle you to bother. They can hold the spark you need to discover and enjoy what's next.

If I were writing the story of my life, the scenes I would have to include are...

What interest, curiosity, or obsession,
never leaves me, at least for long?

I have often thought my interest in
was important and wonderful, but it never seemed to matter in
this noisy world.

If I could solve one problem or lack
in the world, just one, it would be...

SIGNATURE THEMES

The themes of the
books I buy

The themes of the
course I take

What do all
these have in common?
Not the content, the themes.

The themes of the films
and TV I watch

The themes of the retreats
and vacations I take

Other careers, jobs, professions I
could imagine myself doing...

These all have in common...

SIGNATURE THEMES

If you look back at what you wrote on page 93 about living your values, do you notice any overlap between your values and your signature themes? Or any clues to how your signature themes help you live your values?

If you look back at your desires, do you see any themes that emerge or any overlap with what you wrote in this section?

If you asked someone close to you to describe your signature themes, what do you think they would say?

Now, and only now, go ask three people you trust.

SIGNATURE THEMES

When I asked women in the weekly Oasis community about their themes, they shared:

"fascination with depth, mystery, and devotion to creating beauty"

"facilitating excellence"

"celebrating resiliency and continuous growth"

"finding and nurturing the holy and sacred in the ordinary and the everyday"

"saving relationships"

"gathering and sharing information with others"

"everything I do ends up having something to do with child abuse"

On this page, note, in words, images, or photos, one to three key themes of yours.

What if your signature themes are a love note from life itself?
What if all you have to do is listen for them, open a window to them?
What if all they want is for you to love them?

HUMAN-SCALED LIFE

To be embodied is to realize that you have limits. 24 hours in a day. Gravity holding you to the Earth. The need to eat food and drink water. The need for sleep, alone time, beauty, and human connection. Sometimes we want to pretend we don't have limits, but this often leads to exhaustion, overproviding, lack of boundaries, and overwhelm.

The truth is you can't do everything, experience everything, take care of everybody, manage everything, and do everything that needs to be done... ever.

Getting your bother on needs you to work with this fact. To stop denying you have limits and to work within your human-scaled life, time and energy, not denying it or always wishing you could do it all now and faster to boot.

What if life gives me limits to work with like an artist chooses a particular medium, a particular palette, to express her creativity?

My current limits include...

HUMAN-SCALED LIFE

What might I need to change, let go, or do less of to live a human-scaled life that respect my limits more often?

Do I ever push past my limits? When? Why?

What are the signs that I might be doing this?
Common signs are overproviding, exhaustion, fatigue,
lack of time for desires, and feeling resentful.

What is the cost to me?

HUMAN-SCALED LIFE

What limit or limits do I wish I could adjust my life and schedule to accommodate or to be more at peace with?

CONDITIONS OF ENOUGHNESS

I created a tool many years ago called Conditions of Enoughness. The idea is simple and profound: if you never declare what is enough for you, you'll never be satisfied.

We live in a world where everyone else tells us what would be enough—from celebrities to brands selling us things to social media. We also live in a world where we often have to meet other people's standards, whether that is a boss, a client, or a customer. The combined effect can mean we become people who live to succeed, to please, to fix, to caretake, to someday get it all done and finally be able to rest, yet that day never seems to arrive.

We may find we live in a constant shadow of not enoughness that chills us until we don't know how to warm ourselves at the fire of our own desires and presence. We sometimes feel inherently less than. Not enough. When nothing could be further from the truth.

Conditions of Enoughness (COEs) give you a precise way to declare what is enough—you and nobody else—and train your brain to rest. COEs feed self-trust and give self-compassionate grit a ground to work from.

COEs have 4 elements:

1. Name what is enough, according to you, in facts.

That means they are free from opinion, assessment, and outcome. You can do this for anything—writing, a family dinner, a work report, exercise, decluttering, anything.

2. Decide for how long, how often, or some other measurement.

Once a week, for an hour, before bed for a month, my target heart rate, during my commute, Fridays from Memorial Day to Labor Day.

A measurement is the clearest way to know when to stop and say, "That was enough."

3. Be sure what you are declaring is possible for you, given you're a human and not a robot.

Are you asking too much of yourself given your energy level, your to-do list, your previously scheduled commitments? Declaring what is enough means you remember your human-scaled life.

4. When you finish what you said you would do, acknowledge yourself.

Celebrate in some small way. Say to yourself, "Good job." Keep your focus not on how you performed but on celebrating that you did what you said you would. What you declared is enough.

CONDITIONS OF ENOUGHNESS

Think of one area of your life where the feeling of not doing enough creeps in. Managing clutter, exercising, keeping up with email... For today, in just this one area, name what is enough, according to you, in facts. Instead of focusing on meeting an outside standard (which are often vague and impossible to meet), declare your own. "I will clean the kitchen counter of everything but the blender and coffee maker."

What is enough for me today:

Choose a measurement.
"I will clean the counter by dinner time on Sunday."

My measurement is:

Is this possible?
Be sure what you are declaring is possible for you by you, given you're a human and not a robot. If you're making dinner for six people, maybe it's not the day to clean the counter.

Adjust if needed:

Acknowledge yourself.
Keep your focus not on how you performed or what's in the future. Not "But there's so much more clutter" instead, "I did what I said I would do! Yay me!"

I celebrated by:

Think of an area of your life where you experience being dissatisfied with your performance or quality of your efforts. Presentations at work? Writing? How much TV you watch? Standing up for yourself? Instead of focusing on reaching some perfect pinnacle, declare what is enough for this week and keep your focus there. "I will practice my presentation skills by watching TED talks and making notes."

What is enough for me this week:

Choose a measurement.
"I spend 30 minutes watching during my lunch time.
Afterward, I will write down one thing I want to try next week."

My measurement is:

Is this possible?
Be sure what you are declaring is possible, given how much is already going on in your life and dependent only on you, not on an outcome where someone else is pleased or satisfied.

Adjust if needed:

Acknowledge yourself *and celebrate in some way. "Every day after*
I make my notes, I will text my wife to tell her I'm amazing."

I celebrated by:

CONDITIONS OF ENOUGHNESS

Think of one thing you've been procrastinating on—something that feels overwhelming, daunting, boring, difficult, or just ick.

I've been procrastinating on:

To be satisfied this task is finished: *Make a list of what you need to do to be satisfied. Stick with facts. "Empty storage unit." "Take papers to free paper shredding day at the bank."*

Break what needs to be done into smaller steps, each one of which you know how to do. For example, empty storage unit becomes, "Ask five friends for boxes, ask Jennie if I can borrow her truck for Saturday, pack water and snacks, ask Bob to help for two hours."

My small steps for today:

Celebrate every single step you take. Especially if you don't feel like it.

I celebrated by:

COEs help you build self-trust because you are making clear promises and then celebrating that you did what you said you would do. But that won't happen if you declare more COEs than you can complete in a time frame or when life happens and things fall apart, you beat yourself up.

How will I reestablish trust with myself using COEs, when I don't or can't keep my promises to myself?

CONDITIONS OF ENOUGHNESS

Where or when might I be afraid to declare what is enough according to me? Where do I believe satisfaction belongs to someone else's standards or finish line other than mine?

GROWTH MINDSET

You've possibly heard of the growth mindset based on decades of research by Dr. Carol Dweck and her colleagues. Dweck's research taught me how to learn. Which in many ways is what getting your bother on is all about. Desire is the starting point, and it can only flourish and become part of your life through the delight of learning.

The upshot of Dweck's research is you hold two views about yourself: the fixed mindset and the growth mindset, "the view you adopt for yourself profoundly affects the way you lead your life. It can determine whether you become the person you want to be and whether you accomplish the things you value."

When you're in a fixed mindset, you assume your talent, your intelligence, even your moral character are fixed and can't change very much. Any success you experience is a confirmation of who you are, an affirmation of your inherent worth. As are your failures and mistakes. You learn to avoid taking risks and making mistakes so you can maintain your sense of being smart, being enough, and for some of us (me) feeling special. The fixed mindset is what convinces you there is no reason to bother, because you can't do anything differently anyway.

A growth mindset, on the other hand, is the mindset you cultivate when you believe your talent, intelligence, and moral character can be nurtured through effort. When you want something, go for it and it doesn't work or it's much harder than you thought it would be, instead of giving up or getting by, you brainstorm how to learn. You remember you can always develop your talents and abilities. Little about you, or your future, is fixed.

GROWTH MINDSET

The times where the fixed mindset most contributes to me
not getting my bother on... *For example, promoting your work,
speaking a foreign language, trying a new sport.*

Read what you wrote and notice how these mindsets aid your emotional
immune system in keeping you defended. Reframe any feeling of "I suck" or "I
have to change" with "What mindset would help me get more of what I want?"
Try to stay out of the self-improvement mindset and feel your way into the
growth mindset; that's a subtle but vital difference. The former is based on, "If
I just change X or Y about myself, then I will be good enough or able enough,"
while the latter is based on the life-giving fact you can always learn and grow.

It can be helpful to have growth mindset rejoinders to inspire you making up your own. Notice the following examples are not positive affirmations but factual statements that remind you learning and growth are always available.

FIXED MINDSET: I don't know where to start!

GROWTH MINDSET: Sometimes there are several paths as opposed to one perfect route; I'll just pick a reasonable small step and start.

FIXED MINDSET: I don't know if this is going to work. I might fail!

GROWTH MINDSET: I'll know more once I take action and then reflect. I can't know anything until I take action.

FIXED MINDSET: If I were meant to do this, it would be easy. It's not easy, so I am clearly not meant to do it.

GROWTH MINDSET: Who made that rule? "Easy" is another way of saying "why bother?" Easy is boring. Bring it on! I love a challenge.

FIXED MINDSET: I never finish anything. This time won't be any different.

GROWTH MINDSET:That's an exaggeration, and I'll decide what "finishing" looks like for me. I will use conditions of enoughness to decide my next steps.

GROWTH MINDSET

Look back at What I complain about most includes… on page 12.
Choose a few of your complaints and turn them into growth mindset
statements. You don't have to change them all, only the ones you
would genuinely like to do something about.

Complaint	Growth Mindset Statement

Which of my desires need a growth
mindset right now?

Put on a favorite song that makes you feel hopeful, resilient, and brave.
Dance your way into a growth mindset. Let your body show you how to learn.

I made a playlist for you to help you inspire you. Hop on over to jenniferlouden.com/whybother

GROWTH MINDSET

In 2001, I learned about "enemies of learning" in my ontological coaching training. These are the things we believe, and perhaps verbalize, that make it difficult to learn. Enemies of learning are fixed mindset indicators! Enemies of learning and the fixed mindset are one way your emotional immune system keeps you defended.

Read through the following list and circle the sentences that make you nod or cringe and fill in any blanks that speak to you.

I can't _____ .

_____ never works for me.

My sister/brother/best friend/partner is good at _____ .
I'm not. I never will be.

I used to be able to do _____ but not anymore.

If I don't know something, it makes me feel uncomfortable, and then I _____ .

There's really nothing new under the sun. It's all been done.

If you don't know the answer to something immediately, you should quit, because it's a sign you're _____ .

I take multiple courses and earn advanced degrees or certifications, but I rarely claim or benefit from my knowledge.

I identify with a learning disability or shaming story from childhood, high school, or college as proof I can't change or grow.

I'm often dismissive of new technology, different music, or art forms.

I haven't got time to learn   .

I often think or say, "How long is this going to take?"

I often prioritize other people's learning and growth over my own.

I would learn if only I could find someone competent to teach me.

I want to be challenged, I want to learn, but I have such a hard time settling down or staying with things.

If I was willing to be an awkward beginner again then I might try   .

When I want something but aren't sure I can do it, I make jokes about my abilities or pretend I don't really want it.

When someone points out I'm excited and enjoying myself as I learn, I get flustered and want to quit or hide.

It's easier to do everything alone. I rarely ask for help or get mentored.

The biggest reason it's hard for me to learn and grow is...

GROWTH MINDSET

An attitude that can help you embrace the growth mindset is "love the effort." Western culture tends to laud the finish line, but research shows that if you can love the challenge, you enjoy your life more.

The efforts to learn and grow that I am ready to love or am already loving are...

When you find yourself having a difficult time taking action on a desire, self-care or just the crap of life you need to do, try this:

Write down your self-talk—just a few sentences will do.
What is the language of your mood saying?

Notice if what you are telling yourself has a fixed mindset tinge.

Remember your life is yours and action changes mood.
You can always change and grow.

You might write down, "So much more is possible for me!"
Or look back at page 179.

Now feel into what you want.
Feel desire bubbling up in you as energy rising. As life beckoning.

Ask: what's the next simple step I know how to do? Make it small.

Enjoy what happens.

FEAR OF DESIRE

Preparing ahead of time for inner obstacles is a potent way to stay on track with your desires.

What bubbles up within me that holds me back from exploring a desire? *Lack of confidence, getting overwhelmed, overthinking... name these now.*

If _____ (inner obstacle) happens, then I will... *Repeat this for each inner obstacle. Keep whatever you plan super small and simple!*

Examples:

Remind myself I have no idea what I am capable of, and I can always learn.

Do a brain dump of everything I need to do, then choose one small step and do it.

Reach out to a supportive person for an honest, kind pep talk.

Write down all my negative thoughts and ask, "Is this true?"

REFRAMING MINDSET

Notice if you rarely acknowledge what you do or if you always focus on what you didn't get done or that what you did wasn't enough. This is one of the most prevalent ways people drain their energy to bother.

Every time you notice yourself focusing your attention on what you didn't do, or that what you didn't do wasn't enough in some way, come back to this page, make a mark, and write the date.

BODY & HEALTH

Drop into your body with three full, generous breaths. Feel how life is always waiting to infuse you, remind you, and inspire you. Ask your body's wisdom about how getting your bother on is going. Let your body tell you through your non-dominant hand, through movement, or making sound. Make notes here.

EXPAND YOUR EMOTIONAL IMMUNE SYSTEM

Everything in this journal is expanding your emotional immune system, and this exercise will help you put what you've been doing into action.

I want to care about... *Name one desire you hold dear, that you truly want. All that matters is you truly want it. For example: building my business*

What I do instead of exploring this desire is... *Look for things that go against what you want, competing commitments we talked about on page 36. Examples: playing Clash of Clans until 2 am instead of researching my customer's needs, or reading about writing but not writing.*

EXPAND YOUR EMOTIONAL IMMUNE SYSTEM

If I care about   (your one desire), I'm afraid that (name your biggest, hottest fears) will happen and that means (what's the worst possible outcome for you?).

Repeat this prompt as many times as it takes to get on paper your truly biggest fears and your most dreaded outcomes. It doesn't matter if your mind says, "I know that won't happen, I won't end up alone in a Motel 6 with 27 cats." Listen instead to what your gut says, what makes your breath catch. This can sometimes take a few attempts to get to the bedrock "oh that's it," so come back here until you feel you've rung it all out.

It can be uncomfortable and jarring to see your biggest fears associated with your deepest desires, so offer yourself some healthy soothing now. Let yourself pause here for a day or three.

NANO-EXPERIMENTS

Take what you wrote for "If I care about, I'm afraid that…" and design a nano-experiment that tests **one** worst-case scenario in a **small**, safe way and gives you data to ask, "Am I okay? Is it safe to keep going? To take another action on my desire?"

You're testing your model of reality, creating an experiment that could cast doubt on your belief that it's not safe to take action on your desire. You are not trying to prove yourself wrong or jolly yourself out of your fears! It's about witnessing yaour emotional immune system in action while taking one small, safe action that can expand the range of what you can comfortably do. What might these nano-experiments look like?

A nano-experiment for "If I care about starting my business, I'm afraid that I'll spend all my savings and fail" could be, "I will sign up for three reputable free sources of business advice for my field." Then you check in: did I spend any money? This may sound too small to matter, but you will be amazed how repeating these kinds of nano-experiments will expand your view of what's safe to try.

My nano-experiment for today:

EXPAND YOUR EMOTIONAL IMMUNE SYSTEM

Nano-experiments can be repeated until you feel more room to move toward what you want. Record here all the nano-experiments you try and what data you gather. Remember it's not about proving yourself wrong or right and not about making yourself believe anything; it's always about gathering data, which can be anything that happens, how others react, how you feel, or the fact that you did not spontaneously combust.

REASONS TO BOTHER

Because life is not a problem to be solved,
I want to experience...

And I want to share it with...

be seen

The Be Seen stage of getting your bother on is about coming out of hiding with your desires and sharing your experiments. People need a connection to other humans as much as they do food and water. Human brains need to interact with the world. Everyone needs human interconnection to be whole—which is why solitary confinement quickly becomes a form of torture. You might deny your need for others, resist it, have to work through trauma to repair your ability to connect, but without it, you can't thrive. You can't bother when you are all alone. You need to give your gifts to others and have your caring and purpose witnessed.

Open the door to your beauty and power and let others that you trust see you caring. How you do this is up to you—it may be intimate and quiet, or public and shiny. It doesn't matter one whit as long as you come out of hiding and let yourself be seen.

When you don't let yourself be seen bothering, you send yourself the message you don't matter and that what you desire—and the very act of desiring itself—doesn't matter. You're telling yourself, in effect, that it's not important to move forward with your life.

When you let yourself be seen caring, moving forward, and desiring in the ways and time you choose, so much good happens. When you share what matters to you—without hiding, downplaying, or puffing up—what you care about takes on a depth, a vibrancy, a concreteness. You gain energy, clarity, and perhaps refine or expand your what's next.

When you let yourself be seen creating what you want or desiring and exploring, you also increase your self-trust. You aren't looking for someone to say, "I approve." Not at all. You're saying, "Hey, this is what I'm caring about, experimenting with, and I wanted you to share this. There is nothing weird or shameful about being in the 'why bother?' cycle. There's nothing bad about experimenting."

Of course, you might be choosing less doing. You may be doing less than you have in years. That's extra powerful to let others see, because we live in such an overachievement-focused world.

GIFTS & STRENGTHS

Where, when, and with whom do I feel most comfortable shining my light, sharing my desires, offering my strengths, being my full self? *Consider adding pictures of the people and situations where you feel safe and comfortable—or where you would like to feel safe and comfortable.*

If you don't have enough names to add here, write in another color ink who you would like to be seen by—let yourself imagine. Perhaps a new friend, a spiritual mentor, a particular type of person, who would be the most nurturing witnesses for you?

CHOOSING IS YOUR ART

What thrills me about being seen...

What freaks me out...

FEAR OF BEING SEEN

What are you afraid to be seen wanting, taking action on, experimenting with, or enjoying?

And by whom? Who might judge you, demean you, now or in the past? Whose voice might be warning, "Don't get a big head" or "Who do you think you are?" Are you willing to put these people and stories out of your head for now? If so, write their names on banana peels, or leftover pizza boxes, or whatever you have on hand, and take them to a public garbage can. Throw them away while proclaiming, "You have no power over me any longer."

Who (living or dead) might I feel I am betraying or leaving behind, if I am seen growing, flourishing, desiring, caring?

ASKING FOR FEEDBACK

Being seen doesn't mean you invite or accept opinions or feedback unless you genuinely are ready, and you think carefully about whose feedback and what kind of feedback would be useful. Please don't do what I did and run around looking for someone to tell you what to do. I hired coaches and business consultants, consulted psychics, and begged colleagues for their opinions. This isn't being seen or seeing yourself. This is looking for someone to rescue you, approve of you, or tell you what to do.

The ways I've tried to be seen or supported in the past that I want to avoid now...

It might be tempting at this stage to ask the wrong person for feedback, because you are hungry for approval or want to share a growing sense of energy or excitement. Before you ask anyone in any situation for any kind of feedback, no matter how small, consider making a few notes:

Is this person competent to give the feedback I want? Do they have the experience, background, bandwidth, and inner wisdom?

Why am I asking for feedback? What do I hope to learn or gain? *Wanting approval and to know something is a good idea is very human but if you don't hear what you want to hear, what will happen to your spirits? Your determination? Why might you be giving this person this power?*

What feedback do I want to give myself first? *Self-trust is fostered when we acknowledge and see ourselves first.*

COMPANIONSHIP & COMMUNITY CARE

Who might I inspire by being seen growing, flourishing, desiring, and caring?

Who do I want to inspire?

SIGNATURE THEMES

Who could I share my signature theme with? *If you skipped those prompts or didn't come up with a clear theme or two, who could you share the prompts with, explore them side by side, and discuss? Sometimes you need to work on these ideas with another human!*

HOW I BOTHER NOW

How am I becoming more satisfied and engaged with life? What do I see myself doing, saying, feeling?

With desire?

With self-acceptance?

With making and keeping clear promises to myself?

Who do I want to share this satisfaction and engagement with?

COMPANIONSHIP & COMMUNITY CARE

Seeing other people is fantastic for helping you believe in your ability to bother. Over the next week or so, make a point to ask about, champion, or share resources with someone in support of their desires. Come back here and write down what you did and how it felt. Do only if and when you feel like it, no sense of obligation or over giving or caretaking, please.

I Supported

How it Felt

SHADOW COMFORTS & TIME MONSTERS

Are any of my shadow comforts or time monsters a substitute for connecting and being seen? What might be more fulfilling even if it means risking being disappointed or rejected? A very effective ways to deal with stress is to connect with someone. Can you do so now in a small way?

I recorded a short audio mediation to help you see yourself.
It's waiting for you at jenniferlouden.com/whybother.

BEING

Imagine yourself standing before what you hold sacred—being seen by all that you hold dear and acknowledge as vaster than your own mind and identity. Perhaps that is the Divine or nature or science or love or all of these and more rolled up together.

Let yourself feel this energy, this vastness, as a space that both sees you and holds you.

Imagine leaning back on all that supports you, imagine letting go of all the tension in your body, imagine not having to hide, manage, or be any different than you are in this moment.

Imagine all of you, all of your wounds and dents, all of your glory and light, all of your pettiness and all the moments you dug deep, all your self-compassionate grit and self-trust, being seen.

Being loved.

Being welcome.

All that you hold dear surrounding you. "I see you."

always
begin again

One warm July afternoon at the Mabel Dodge Luhan House in Taos, New Mexico, I was leading a writing retreat and talking about the power of "begin again," how having the self-compassionate grit to start over—whether you stopped or something stopped you—is the most helpful idea and one of the most difficult to allow ourselves. What we often do is dodge the fact we stopped, try to figure out why we stopped, wait for our life circumstances to change, or make a complicated plan for how to never fall off the wagon again. Then we stick to our plan for a couple of days, only to quit and feel defeated.

Ruth, a writer and photographer who had attended my retreats for years, took me aside after class. "There's something I learned in the Benedictine tradition, Jen, that you might like. 'Always we begin again.'"

I rocked back and forth in my Birkenstocks. "Always?"

"As in have mercy on yourself. You'll always lose your way, give up, doubt yourself. It's inevitable. So don't be surprised by it. Always begin again."

Always. What a miraculous word. Stop expecting yourself to be steady, consistent, uniform, perfect, or otherwise robot-like in anything. You will always have to begin again—and that includes bothering.

You will always have to begin again. Embrace this truth, and you'll always be able to get your bother on. Always be able to change the trajectory of your day, and your life.

Put on a song, move, and feel the truth that you can always begin again.

HOW I BOTHER NOW

I notice I am not bothering about   anymore.

And that feels...

What helps me begin again includes...

A song, talking it out with a friend, long walk a day doing exactly what you want...

HOW I BOTHER NOW

Distill what bothering looks and feels like for you. When you're caring in a way that's deeply satisfying, calm, self-trusting, energized, alert, open to wonder, and tuned to the growth mindset, how would you describe that kind of bothering? Play with any of these questions to get started:

If your style of bothering were a color,
what color would it be?
Find a bit of that color and add it here.

What mode of transportation?
Hiking boots, bullet train,
Porsche convertible, donkey...
Paste a picture or make a doodle.

What geographic location?
It can be an imaginary place,
made up by you or someone else.
Find a picture or make a tiny collage.

What character from a movie,
TV show, or book is similar
to you in how they bother?

Might there be a poem, a quotation,
a line of scripture, a sutra that encapsulates
your preferred way of bothering?
Find it and name it here.

HOW I BOTHER NOW

What are five actions you take when you're getting your bother on your way? Mine are pausing (to feel, to settle, to welcome), moving my body (stretching, dancing, making noise), journaling (using this journal), disrupting a routine that has become deadening, and connecting with people even if I don't feel like it.

keep going

Bothering again—the way you want—doesn't fit into any box. You can't hold it up for someone else to say, "Oh you did it, good job." It's far richer and more subtle. It's also more ineffable and personal, and yet, at the same time, universal. Because how could living the adventure of your full and awakened life be anything but?

Getting your bother on is trusting that life is rising in you. It's settling down more often to be in life and in your life. It's encouraging yourself instead of shutting down or giving up. It's delighting in wonder more often. It's noticing and being curious about your big and small desires, even when you can't have them. It's venturing past the known by testing your assumptions about what you must do to stay defended. It's being kinder to yourself. It's tickling your lovely self awake with a growth mindset and replacing shadow comforts and substitute desires more of the time.

It's knowing you can always begin again.

It's living *your* life, the one you want now instead of the one you think you have to wait for.

And then, as you die, you will not be wondering who you could have become, what you could have experienced, who you could have loved, or what you could have shared, created, savored.

Keep this journal around, look back at it when *"why bother?"* comes sneaking around. Add to it in celebration of how you continually grow, rather than how you don't yet have it figured out.

Use it to remind yourself and to celebrate all that you are, are always becoming, and that you truly can, and do, get your bother on.

Keep Getting your Bother On

Have you read the book that started it all? *Why Bother? Discover the Desire for What's Next* is available wherever books are sold and on Audible—read by me, complete with tears.

Be sure and collect your gifts, my thank you for using this journal. They await you at jenniferlouden.com/why-bother

For help bringing the ideas in this book alive and continuing to get your bother on, join me and a community of like-minded people at the Oasis, the online recharging station that keeps your desires and your courage alive week after week. It's where we live the ideas in this journal through weekly audio retreats, monthly live events, regular community check ins, and sometimes, dance parties. **Join the Oasis** at jenniferlouden. com/writers-oasis

Get weekly reminders by subscribing to my newsletter. This is also where I announce retreats (online and in person), new books, and live journaling events using this journal. Get the newsletter by sauntering over to jenniferlouden.com/newsletter. It's free.

Jennifer Louden wanted to be Harriet the Spy when she was eight, an enlightened master when she was twelve, and a brilliant comedy writer when she was twenty-two. She penned her first bestseller, *The Woman's Comfort Book*, after her first "why bother?" time. She's the author of five additional books including *The Woman's Retreat Book* and *The Life Organizer*. This guided journal is the companion to her newest book, *Why Bother? Discover the Desire for What's Next*, available wherever books are sold and on Audible.

Jen has inspired millions of women through her books, her retreats and workshops, and her blog, but probably not with her fashion sense and certainly not her cooking.

She lives in Colorado with her husband Bob and wishes her grown kids would move around the corner.

List of Prompts and Page Numbers

CPSIA information can be obtained
at www.ICGtesting.com
Printed in the USA
BVHW012228171220
595904BV00014B/296